S0-CAD-869

Reader's Digest READING SKILL BUILDER

SILVER EDITION EDITORS

Miriam Weiss Meyer and Peter Travers, Project Editors

Sally Berke, Editor

SILVER EDITION CONSULTANTS

Fred Chavez, Director of Programs
Los Angeles City Reading Support Services Center
Los Angeles, California

Marguerite E. Fuller, Assistant Supervisor of Language Arts
Norwalk Public Schools
Norwalk, Connecticut

Sister Maria Loyola, I.H.M., Chairperson, Reading Curriculum Committee
Archdiocese of Philadelphia
Philadelphia, Pennsylvania

Dr. John. F. Savage, Coordinator, Reading Specialist Program
Boston College, School of Education
Chestnut Hill, Massachusetts

Richard B. Solymos, Reading Resource Teacher
School Board of Broward County
Fort Lauderdale, Florida

READER'S DIGEST EDUCATIONAL DIVISION
© 1977 by Reader's Digest Services, Inc., Pleasantville, N.Y. 10570. All rights reserved, including
the right to reproduce this book or parts thereof in any form.
Printed in the United States of America.
Reader's Digest ® Trademark Reg. U.S. Pat. Off. Marca Registrada ISBN 0-88300-404-6

TF 702-02

■ **Part 2.**

Property of
Irving Independent School District
Irving, Texas
T1-PL89-10

Silver Edition

STORIES

📼 Stories for which Audio Lessons are available.
RDX number indicates RDX card for that story.

Irving Independent School District
Irving, Texas
TT-FI-35-10

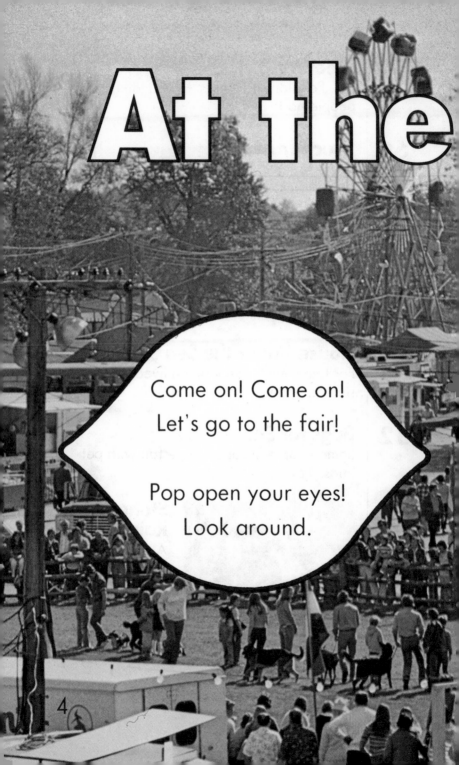

At the

Come on! Come on!
Let's go to the fair!

Pop open your eyes!
Look around.

4

Fair

Key Words
whirling
wiggle
woolly
pizza

See shapes and colors.
Watch people having fun.
Find out which dog
will win first prize.

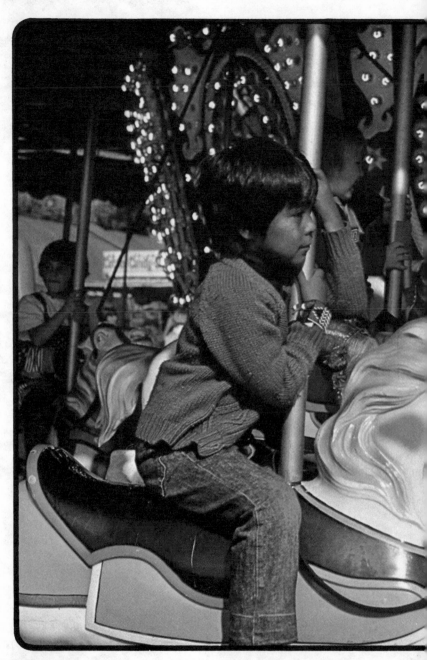

Wake up your ears.
Listen to the music
of the whirling
merry-go-round.
Hear the rush
of race cars
roaring by.

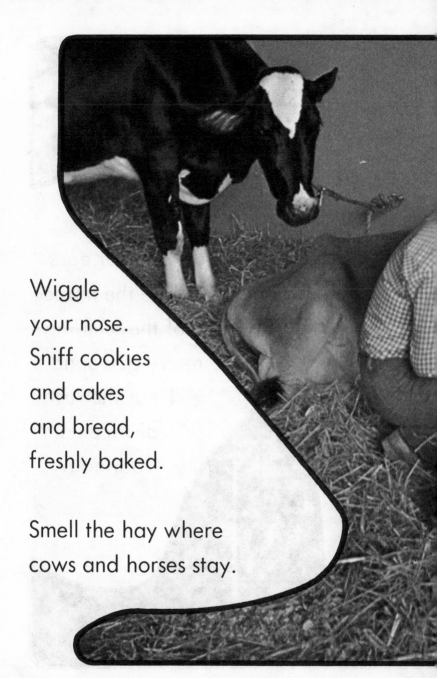

Wiggle
your nose.
Sniff cookies
and cakes
and bread,
freshly baked.

Smell the hay where
cows and horses stay.

8

Reach out your hand.
Pick at a sticky ball
of cotton candy.

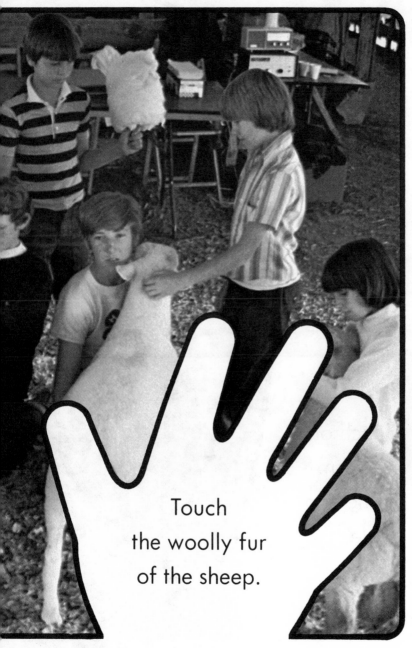

Touch
the woolly fur
of the sheep.

Open your mouth and taste some treats.

Munch on popcorn. Crunch an apple.

12

Get hot dogs
and pizza pie
to share.

Come on!
Come on!
Have fun
at the fair.

13

Remember the Fair   *author's purpose*

What is this story about?
Circle two answers.

1. fun at the circus
2. things to see, hear, smell, feel and taste
3. fun at the fair
4. the new zoo

⚷ 12 • Best score 2 • My score ....

Taste Treats   *classification / outline*

Circle four things you can <u>taste.</u>

a. apple
b. ice cream
c. hot dog
d. race cars
e. popcorn
f. merry-go-round

⚷ 113 • Best score 4 • My score ....

Wonder about Words   *vocabulary*

Read the first word in each group.
Then circle another word in that
group that tells about the first word.
One is done for you.

1. merry-go-round
   a. (whirling)
   b. little

2. race car
   a. roaring
   b. sweet

3. sheep
   a. roaring
   b. woolly

4. cotton candy
   a. loud
   b. sticky

🔑 86 • Best score 4 • My score ....
All Best Scores 10 • All My Scores ....

Look Around   *graphics*

What things in the story pictures do
you like best? Why? Name other
things in the pictures you can see,
hear, smell, feel and taste.

15

Let's Paint the Town !

Little jars of colors
were passed
around the room.
"Let's paint pictures
of our town,"
said Miss Parker,
the teacher.

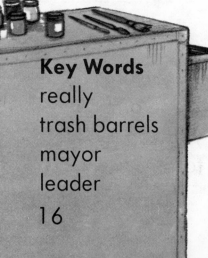

Key Words
really
trash barrels
mayor
leader
16

"Let's <u>really</u> paint our town!"
joked Penny. The class laughed.

"Why not?" asked Luis. "We always
just paint on paper. Let's paint
something that everyone in Sunville
can see!"

Girls and boys shouted ideas!
"Let's paint faces on the school!"
"Let's paint telephone poles!"
"Let's paint a bus!"

"Trash barrels!" cried Andy.
"We could paint them bright colors."

"That sounds good!" said Miss Parker.
"First we should ask the mayor. He's
    the leader of Sunville."
18

The mayor loved the idea. He helped
bring the barrels to school.

The class began painting barrels.
"Sunville will be the brightest town
on the map!" said Glen.

Glen was right! There were
smiling faces in the park. There were
big yellow spots outside the bank.
A bright barrel dotted each corner.

Everyone loved the barrels.

Many people sent letters to the class.

One letter made the class smile.

The mayor wrote it. He said,

"Thank you for your help.

Now Sunville looks better than ever!"

Sunville
School

Be Bright *supporting details*

Draw a line under three things that happened in the story.

1. The mayor wrote a letter.

2. The class painted trash barrels.

3. The class painted a bus.

4. The mayor liked the trash barrels.

🔑66 • Best score 3 • My score ....

Paint a Check *inferences*

Check (✔) four true sentences.

_____ 1. The town had many trash barrels.
_____ 2. Miss Parker was a teacher.
_____ 3. The mayor was helpful.
_____ 4. Miss Parker was angry.
_____ 5. The class got many letters.

🔑117 • Best score 4 • My score ....

What Came First? *sequence*

Put 1 by the thing that came first in the story. Put 2 by the thing that came next. Put 3 by the thing that came last.

Dear Class:
The Mayor

Paint

_____

_____

_____

Your Town *role play*

Think of a way your class can help your town. What things will you need?

**Key
Words**
guitar
bowed

24

Just for Three?

Segovia (seh-<u>goh</u>-vyuh)
plays the guitar. Many
people think he is the best
guitar player in the world.
People fill large rooms to
hear him.

One night Segovia asked his helper,
"Where will my show be tonight?"

"Come with me. I'll take you there,"
the helper said. They drove
to a woman's house.

Segovia met the woman
at her front door. He asked,
"Where are all the people
who paid to hear me?"

The woman said,
"There are only my two
friends and I. I love your music. I'll
pretend this is a big room filled with
people. And I'll pay for all of them."

Segovia was surprised! "I've
never put on a show for just three
people! But I can."

He sat down. His fingers danced across his guitar. Beautiful music filled the small room.

He played all his songs. Then he bowed. His three listeners clapped.

"This was a different kind of show," he said. "But I liked it. I liked it very much. Thank you for letting me play for you."

A Special Show *sequence*

There is a 1 by the sentence that tells what Segovia did first. Put 2, 3 and 4 by the other sentences to show when they happened.

_____ He bowed.

_____ He played for three people.

__1__ He drove to a woman's house.

_____ He met the woman at her door.

🔑 105 · Best score 4 · My score ....

Music Match *graphics*

Write each word below its picture.

1. guitar   2. clap   3. bow

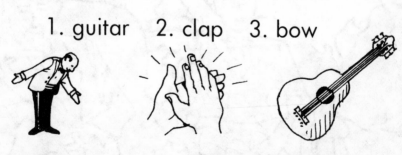

_____   _____   _____

🔑 54 · Best score 3 · My score ....

Voices   *points of view*

Who might say each thing? Pick from these people.

a. Segovia
b. the helper
c. the woman

Who . . .   Might Say This?

_____   "I'll take you to your show."
_____   "My friends and I like
                    your music."
_____   "Where's my guitar?"

🔑 52 • Best score 3 • My score ....
All Best Scores 10 • All My Scores ....

Something New   *inferences*

Most of the time Segovia played for large groups of people. Why do you think he liked this show for just three people?

31

32

His Little Circus Comes to Life

Take a peek at Bill's circus.
Animals play games. Clowns
jump up and down.
Dancers hang by their toes.

But Bill's circus is quiet.
Sometimes it just hums.

Why don't the animals roar
and clowns yell? The circus is
cut out of wood. Bill carved
all the pieces.

Bill can make his circus come
to life. When he turns on a switch,
the circus whirls. Round and round
it goes. Tigers do tricks.
Strong men lift heavy bars.

Every circus is fun to watch. But
Bill's tiny, wooden circus is special!

Circus Words *supporting details*

Three words below tell about Bill's circus. Circle each word.

1. sad   3. little

2. quiet   4. wood

⚷ 65 • Best score 3 • My score ....

Take a Peek *graphics*

Look at the pictures in this story. Then circle two true sentences.

1. Lots of people watch the circus.

2. Many things happen at once.

3. The circus animals are the same color as real animals.

4. The circus is as big as a house.

⚷ 7 • Best score 2 • My score ....

36

Under the Big Top   *classification/outline*

Which things belong in Bill's circus?
Circle three words.

   1. clowns   3. tricks

   2. animals   4. boats

🗝 55 • Best score 3 • My score ....

Clowns   *summary*

Circle two clown faces that tell what
this story is about.

1

2

3

🗝 12 • Best score 2 • My score ....
All Best Scores 10 • All My Scores ....

The Real Thing   *comparison/contrast*

How is Bill's circus <u>not</u> like a real one?

Key Words
lab
recipes
juice
terrible

"Come into my lab, Tom. I'm
writing a cookbook," said Cora.
"I will dream up great recipes!"

"What's a recipe?" asked Tom.

38

Cora held up a card. "A recipe is a list. It tells how much of each thing to mix together. I am making a new drink. I mix two cups of lemon juice, one cup of apple juice and one cup of salt."

Cora gave Tom a glass.
"Try some!" she said.

Tom took a sip.
"Yikes!" he screamed.

"What's wrong?"
asked Cora.

"Well, you try it,"
said Tom.

Cora took a sip.
"Ugh!" she groaned.
Quickly she flipped
over the card
and wrote—
Tastes Terrible!

New Words *vocabulary*

Put the letter of each word beside its meaning. One is done for you.

a. recipe   c. terrible
b. cookbook   d. lab

_____ a group of recipes
_____ very bad
_____ a room for trying new things
__a__ a list that tells what to mix

🔑 103 • Best score 4 • My score ....

Pick a Recipe *main idea*

Make an X on two cards that tell about the story.

a. Cora's new recipe   b. Cora cooks dinner   c. A terrible drink

🔑 9 • Best score 2 • My score ....

Cora's Story   *supporting details*

Make an X by each right answer.

1. What was Cora doing?
_____ a. writing a cookbook
_____ b. writing a note

2. Who made up the new recipe?
_____ a. Cora
_____ b. Tom

3. Why did Tom scream?
_____ a. He liked the drink.
_____ b. The drink tasted terrible.

4. What was in the new recipe?
_____ a. sugar, milk
_____ b. salt, juice

⚷ 86 • Best score 4 • My score ....
All Best Scores 10 • All My Scores ....

_____

Blah!   *inferences*

Why did Cora's drink taste bad?

43

Baby Animals

Animals don't act like people!
Or do they?

A family has a special kind
of love. Animals have it.
People have it.

How did you learn to walk?
Someone special helped you.
This cub is getting the same
kind of help.

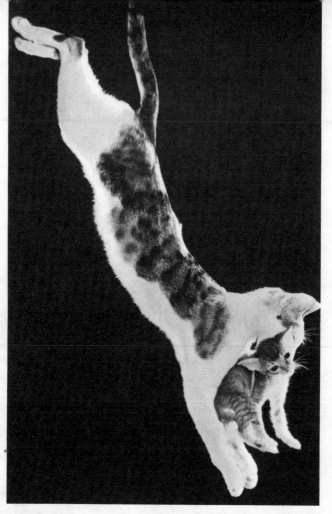

Animal parents keep
their babies safe. This
kitten will be put
into a hiding place.

46

This colt's mother
will stay close by.

Family love is a special feeling.
And no, it's not just for people.

The Story *main idea*

Draw a line under three sentences that tell about this story.

1. Animals feel family love.

2. Family love is a special feeling.

3. People should have pets.

4. Animals keep their babies safe.

5. Animals can talk.

⟜66 • Best score 3 • My score ....

Baby Animals *vocabulary*

Draw a line from each baby to its parent.

a. colt	bear
b. cub	cat
c. kitten	horse

⟜52 • Best score 3 • My score ....

What Is Family Love? *phrase meaning*

Draw a line under four things that show family love.

1. Father teaches baby to walk.

2. Mother watches her babies.

3. Mother hen feeds the chicks.

4. Mother hides from baby.

5. Baby hugs Father.

🗝117 • Best score 4 • My score ....
All Best Scores 10 • All My Scores ....

People Families *comparison / contrast*

How do parents keep their children safe?

How do brothers and sisters help each other?

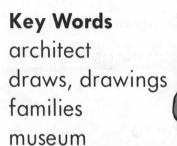

Meet
Mr. Pei

52

I. M. Pei (pay) is an architect.
He sees buildings in his mind.

He draws them on paper.
The drawings show
a builder what to build.

Mr. Pei thinks about many things.
"What is in the building?
What do the people need?"

People in office buildings need
quiet rooms for work. Mr. Pei
draws lots of small rooms. This way
each person may work alone.

Families in tall buildings need
space to play. Mr. Pei draws grass
and trees by each building. Now
the families have a yard.

Mr. Pei wants his buildings to look different. He once made a drawing of a museum. He didn't make just one building. He made four. He showed bridges between the buildings. He showed a park in the middle.

Mr. Pei has won prizes for his ideas. His buildings are beautiful. They make people happy.

About the Story *supporting details*

Circle the right words.

1. An architect ____ buildings.
   a. draws   b. tears down

2. Mr. Pei's museum had four ____.
   a. parks   b. buildings

3. The buildings make people ____.
   a. sad   b. happy

⚷ 41 • Best score 3 • My score ....

Mr. Pei *characterization*

Circle three sentences that tell about Mr. Pei.

   1. He cares about people.
   2. He likes to be different.
   3. He carries bricks.
   4. He has won many prizes.

⚷ 66 • Best score 3 • My score ....

58

Build a Group   *classification/outline*

Circle two words that belong in each group.

Kinds of Buildings
1. office
2. museum
3. tree

Things Outdoors
4. yard
5. desk
6. park

⚷ 123 • Best score 4 • My score ....
All Best Scores 10 • All My Scores ....

Be an Architect   *role play*

Think about your school. Would you build it differently? If so, how?

Space Trucks

Some people drive cars to work.
Some ride buses. Some go by trains.
But soon things will change.
Some people will zoom to work
in space trucks!

Key Words
machines
Earth
special

61

A space truck will blast off!
It will carry people and
machines above the Earth.

People will work in the space truck.
Some will look at stars. Some will look
for special rocks and plants on Earth.

62

For many days, the people
will live and work in space.

Then the truck will return
to Earth. It will land on the
ground like an airplane.
The people will go home
until the next blast-off.

Blast Off! *summary*

What did you learn about the space truck? Circle three sentences.

1. People will work in it.

2. It will blast off.

3. It will fly through space.

4. It will land on buildings.

⚷ 55 • Best score 3 • My score ....

Off We Go! *classification/outline*

Circle three things that people now ride to work.

1. car
2. bus
3. star
4. train

⚷ 66 • Best score 3 • My score ....

Another Truck *comparison/contrast*

Put A by each sentence that tells about this kind of

Put B by each sentence that tells about a

_____ It drives up the street.
_____ It flies.
_____ It parks outside your house.
_____ It lands like an airplane.

84 • Best score 4 • My score ....
All Best Scores 10 • All My Scores ....

When You Grow Up *prediction*

Would you like to work in a space truck? Why or why not?

Mice Are Nice, But...

Key Words
twins
neighbor
neighborhood

"We have a surprise for you," said Jan.

"Wait right there, Mom," said Dan.
The twins brought out a box. Mother
opened it. She saw ten white mice.

"Our pet mice had babies,"
said Dan. "Now we
have ten pets."

"We can't keep them all," Mother said.
"They will grow too big for the box.
We won't have a place to keep them."

The next day, Mother came home from work. She saw one mouse in the box. "Where are the others?" she asked.

Then the telephone rang. Mrs. Saks was calling from next door. "I found something in my mailbox," she said. "I wonder if you found something, too."

"What is it?" asked Mother.

Mrs. Saks said, "I found a little white mouse. There is a note tied to its tail. The note says, **Please give me a happy home!**"

"Jan! Dan!" Mother called.
"Why does Mrs. Saks
have a mouse?"

Dan pointed out the window. "We
gave a mouse to each neighbor.
That left us with only one mouse.
Now our mouse will have lots of
neighborhood friends to play with."

71

The Mice   *story elements*

Circle the best endings.

1. Mother's surprise was a _____.
   a. box of mice   b. candy bar

2. The twins gave away _____.
   a. all the mice   b. nine mice

3. Mrs. Saks found a mouse in _____.
   a. her mailbox   b. a tree

4. The twins gave the mice to the _____.
   a. teacher   b. neighbors

⌐84 · Best score 4 · My score ....

People   *classification/outline*

Which words are words for <u>people</u>?
Circle two.

   1. neighbors   3. pets
   2. tails   4. twins

⌐22 · Best score 2 · My score ....

72

Who Might Say This?   *points of view*

Who might say each thing? Pick from these people.

a. Dan
b. Mother
c. Jan
d. Mrs. Saks

<u>Who . . .</u>   <u>Might Say This?</u>

_____ "We can't keep the mice."
_____ "Dan and I had ten mice."
_____ "Why do I have this mouse?"
_____ "Jan, let's surprise Mother."

🔑 103 • Best score 4 • My score ....
All Best Scores 10 • All My Scores ....

Now What?   *prediction*

Do you think Mrs. Saks kept the mouse? Why or why not? How would you have found homes for the mice?

73

Sea

What is it like to live in the ocean? Five women wanted to find out. They moved to a ''house'' under water.

The house was only as big as a large tent. The house sat on the ocean floor. The women lived there for 14 days.

How do sea
animals live?
How do sea plants
grow? The women
wanted to know.

Each day the women swam outside the house. They found out about the sea.

After each swim,
the women wrote
about the things
they saw.

They talked.
They ate.
They read books.

The women
learned many
things. Most of
all, they learned
how it feels to
live close together
in a house under
the sea.

78

Swim Around   *supporting details*

Circle the best endings.

1. The women lived _____.
   a. under water   b. at the beach

2. They learned about _____.
   a. the sea   b. boats

3. They lived in the house for _____.
   a. 14 years   b. 14 days

4. The house was as big as a _____.
   a. truck   b. tent

⚷ 86 • Best score 4 • My score ....

Splash In!   *classification/outline*

Circle two <u>ocean</u> words.

1. paper   2. sea   3. water

⚷ 12 • Best score 2 • My score ....

Under Water   *summary*

Circle four things the women did.

1. They swam.

2. They wrote.

3. They looked at sea animals.

4. They danced.

5. They talked.

⌐○ 117 • Best score 4 • My score ....
All Best Scores 10 • All My Scores ....

Tiny Home   *role play*

The women in the underwater house lived very close together. What would you like about living close together? What wouldn't you like?

Bugs for Sale

Key Words

Tokyo, Japan
caught
owner
bought

82

Pretend you live in a big field.
What kind of pet can you have?
You might have an elephant.

Now pretend you live in a tiny house.
Could you squeeze an elephant into
it? No. But a tiny bug could fit.

People in Tokyo, Japan, live in
tiny houses. Many of these city
people have pet bugs.

At first only a few people caught
bugs for pets. Then other people
went bug hunting. Soon no bugs
were left in the city.

One day a store owner had an idea.
"Let's <u>sell</u> bugs! Let's make
a bug park on the store roof!"

The store owner went to the roof. He made a large room. He planted trees and grass. Then he drove out to the country. He drove back with hundreds of bugs.

Many shoppers came to buy the bugs.
They caught their own pets. Some
also bought bug cages and toys.
Some bought books about pet bugs.

Now there are many bug stores in
Japan. The people love pet bugs.
You can see why. Bugs don't bark
or scratch. They don't chase cars.
They don't eat much. Best
of all, they are fun.

Catch the Opposites *vocabulary*

In and out are opposites. What other opposites can you find? Put the letters in the blanks.

___C___ out   a. tiny

_____ large   b. buy

_____ city   c. in

_____ sell   d. many

_____ few   e. country

🔑156 · Best score 5 · My score ....

People in Tokyo *generalizations*

Draw a line under three things that tell about the people in Tokyo.

   1. They are afraid of bugs.
   2. They take good care of pets.
   3. They live in tiny houses.
   4. They like bugs.

🔑65 · Best score 3 · My score ....

88

Pets in Tokyo *cause / effect*

Draw a line under each right answer.

1. Why do the people have tiny pets?
   a. The houses are tiny.
   b. They can't find large pets.

2. Why did the store owner go to the country to catch bugs?
   a. The store was in the country.
   b. There were no bugs left in the city.

🗝2 • Best score 2 • My score ....
All Best Scores 10 • All My Scores ....

Tiny Pets *comparison / contrast*

How would you take care of a pet bug? How would it be different from taking care of a dog or cat?

Stone Rainbow

Rainbow Bridge looks like a rainbow. But it's made of stone. You can find the bridge in Utah.

How did Rainbow Bridge get its name?

Indians still tell
this make-believe story.

Long, long ago, a man
went hunting. It began
to rain very hard. The
rain made a roaring river.
The man could not swim!
He could not get away.

By magic, a rainbow appeared.
It made a bridge over the water.
The man climbed the rainbow.
He was safe. Then the
rainbow turned to stone.
The stone rainbow still
stands today.

People like to tell this story.
But now they know the bridge
was not made by magic.

Rainbow Bridge was made
by the wind. Wind blew sand
against a large rock. The sand
rubbed away at the rock until
it made a large hole. All this
took many, many years.

Today, visitors come to see
Rainbow Bridge. It is a sight
you would not forget.

The sun shines on miles of rock.
Above it, the sky is bright blue.
The stone rainbow stretches
like a giant yawn.

Beautiful Bridge *skimming*

Circle the right endings.

1. Rainbow Bridge is in _____.
   a. Texas   b. Utah

2. The bridge is made of _____.
   a. stone   b. steel

3. The bridge was made by _____.
   a. sunshine   b. wind

⚷ 42 • Best score 3 • My score ....

Old, Old, Old *sentence meaning*

Circle two sentences that tell you the bridge is <u>old</u>.

1. The bridge was made long ago.

2. All this took many, many years.

3. The bridge looks like a rainbow.

⚷ 7 • Best score 2 • My score ....

Make-Believe Story *story elements*

Circle three sentences from the part of the story that's make-believe.

1. The rainbow appeared by magic.
2. The rainbow turned to stone.
3. A man climbed the rainbow.
4. Wind made the bridge.

⟜55 · Best score 3 · My score ....

Word Group *vocabulary*

Circle two words that mean almost the same thing.

a. rock   b. mud   c. stone

⟜9 · Best score 2 · My score ....
All Best Scores 10 · All My Scores ....

Bridges *comparison/contrast*

How is Rainbow Bridge different from this?

96